PRACTICAL CONSTRUCTION OF PRE-AMPS, TONE CONTROLS, FILTERS AND ATTENUATORS

D1476690

by

A.D.M. SMITH, B.Sc.,C.Eng.,M.I.E.R.E.,M.B.K.T.S.

BERNARD BABANI (publishing) LTD
THE GRAMPIANS
SHEPHERDS BUSH ROAD
LONDON W6 7NF
ENGLAND

PLEASE NOTE

© 1979 BERNARD BABANI (publishing) LTD

First Published – June 1979
Reprinted January – 1984

British Library Cataloguing in Publication Data
Smith, A.D.M.
    Practical construction of pre-amps, tone controls,
    filters and attenuators. – (Bernards & Babani Press
    radio and electronics books; 60).
    1. Sound – Recording and reproducing –
    Amateurs' manuals
    I. Title
    621.389'3   TK9968

    ISBN 0 900162 80 5

Printed and Bound in Great Britain by Mayhew McCrimmon Printers Ltd

CONTENTS

SPECIAL NOTES FOR USA READERS

There are slight differences in language, terminology and
component numbering and coding between the UK and
USA. The following notes may be of help to the US reader.

Terminology

English	USA
Earthed	Grounded
Fixing screws	Mounting screws
Centre	Center
Mains	AC supply voltage
Tagboards	Terminal boards
Tags	Terminals/lugs
Screened	Shielded
Smoothing	Filtering
HT (high tension)	High voltage
240 Volts AC	120 Volts AC in USA
Fitting	Installing

Transistors

Book used	US equivalent (JEDEC)
BC108	2N929
BC109	2N930
BC184K	2N5827
BC184L	2N5210
MJE340	2N6177
MPS6518	2N4403
OC70	2N406
OC71	2N406
UT46	UJT
2N3053	2N2297
2N3704	2N3704
2N3706	2N3704
2N3707	2N5210

Section 1

MAGNETIC TAPE RECORDING
PRE-AMPLIFIERS

To begin with, a few words about the principles of Magnetic Tape Recording for those enthusiasts who are not very familiar with the principles and also for those who have forgotten.

When we make a recording, the audio signal (information) is transferred to the oxide coated tape as a series of magnetic patterns. The pattern is usually made up of elements along the width of the tape and a complete sine wave makes two elements of the pattern. The higher the frequency of the recorded signal, the closer the elements of the pattern are situated. The greater the amplitude (the louder the signal) the more flux is induced in the tape. Now, as the frequency of the signal increases, we get to a particular frequency when the wavelength of the signal is equal to the gap width of the replay head, i.e. two elements of the recorded signal are contained in the gap of the replay head. As the replay head cannot "read" any change from one element to the next one, the output drops to zero. This frequency is called the "Extinction Frequency".

There also comes a point when an increase in signal level does not result in an increase in flux on the tape. At this point, we say that we are saturating the tape. But, for good recording practice, we use what is called "A Peak Recording Level" and this is defined as the level of a recorded 1 kHz signal that would produce a given amount of peak distortion. This signal is usually recorded on a special tape and it is used to set up the gain of the replay amplifier of a tape recorder. Such tapes are called "Calibration Tapes", "Standard Tapes", "Alignment Tapes" or "Standard Alignment Tapes". The recommended "Flux Densities" for the different tape speeds are as follows:

19 cm/sec (7½"/sec) . . . . 320 nWb/M
9.5 cm/sec (3¾"/sec) . . . . 250 nWb/M
4.75 cm/sec (1⅞"/sec) . . . . 250 nWb/M

Suppose we have a full track recording of a peak recorded signal (320 nWb/M) on a 6.35 mm (¼") tape; then the flux available at the replay head is

$$320 \times 6.0 \times 10^{-3} = 1.92 \text{ nWb}$$

i.e. flux available = flux density x track width.

If this tape is played back on a half-track machine, the flux available would be

$$320 \times 2.5 \times 10^{-3} = 0.80 \text{ nWb}$$

assuming a track width of 2.5 mm.

Similarly, on a quarter-track machine, the flux available would be

$$320 \times 1.0 \times 10^{-3} = 0.32 \text{ nWb}$$

assuming a track width of 1.0 mm.

As it is the flux that produces the output across the replay head, assuming similar heads, we see that half track would produce 0.80/1.92 or 0.42 of the full track output. Similarly, the quarter track output is 0.32/1.92 or 0.16 of the full track output. Thus the half track and quarter track outputs are roughly 7 dB and 15 dB down respectively compared with the full track output. In general, for the same tape speed, the output gets smaller as the track width is reduced and as a result, the signal to noise gets worse. Suppose we record a tape such that the flux induced on the tape is constant at all frequencies. During playback, we will get an output similar to Fig. 1.1. Initially, the output rises at 6 dB/octave due to the increasing rate of change of flux i.e. as the frequency on the tape increases, the elements of the magnetic pattern are closer together and the flux changes at a faster rate.

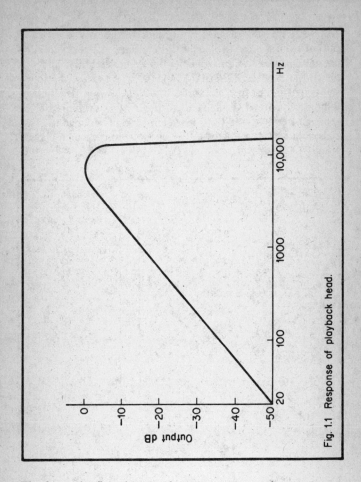

Fig. 1.1 Response of playback head.

The faster the flux changes, the more output we have across the replay head. The output is a maximum at a frequency when the replay head gap width is equal to one-half of the wavelength of the recorded signal. For example, at a tape speed of 19 cm/sec and a replay head gap width of 12 μm, the maximum output occurs at 7.5 kHz. Beyond this point the output begins to fall until it is zero at the extinction frequency. The fall in output is due to self demagnetisation, replay head losses and loss due to bias erasure.

Although we started with a constant recorded flux, the output from the replay head is not constant; hence we have to compensate for the losses in the replay pre-amplifier and hence the need for "EQUALISATION". We boost the low frequency end of the spectrum, so that the output rises with falling frequency. A slight boost is sometimes required at the high frequency end of the spectrum to offset head losses. This could be catered for either in the recording or replay amplifier.

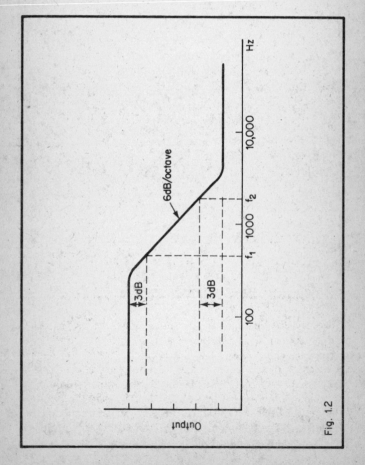

Fig. 1.2

It is usual to quote equalisation characteristics in terms of "Time Constants". A time constant, T, is the production of C and R forming a simple C–R network and T is measured in seconds. T is related to the "Turnover Frequency" by the expression

$$f = 1/2T$$

Fig. 1.2 shows the response of a circuit with two time constants and hence two turnover frequencies.

Some of the requirements of the pre-amplifier can be summarised as follows:

(a) High gain – so that the amplifier can approximate an operational amplifier and then the frequency response and the gain can be determined by the feedback network only.

(b) As the output of most replay heads is around 1 mV, the noise of the amplifier must be low.

(c) The output impedance must be low to act as a take-off point for suitable feedback networks which can have relatively low impedances at high frequencies.

(d) Adequate overload capability as any distortion in the system must occur in the recording medium, i.e. the recording tape, and not in the amplifiers.

Three circuits have been selected because of their performance, ease of assembly and cheapness of components.

(A) Three Transistor Circuit

This is a simple three transistor circuit with the minimum of components (Fig. 1.3). NPN transistors are used in the common emitter mode. C1 is the input capacitor feeding TR1 which forms a high gain stage together with TR2. TR3 is an emitter follower which provides a low output impedance as a suitable take-off point for the feedback network. D.C. feedback is employed from TR2 emitter, decoupled by C5, to the base of TR1 via R1. DC coupling is used throughout the amplifier, except TR3 which is A.C. coupled to the output terminal. A.C. feedback is applied between the emitter of TR1 and the emitter of TR3. R10, C6 together with R4, or R5 or R6 provide an increasing response with falling frequency. The turnover frequency at the high frequency end is dependent on the selection of R4, R5 or R6; thus providing equalisation at the three speeds of 19, 9.5

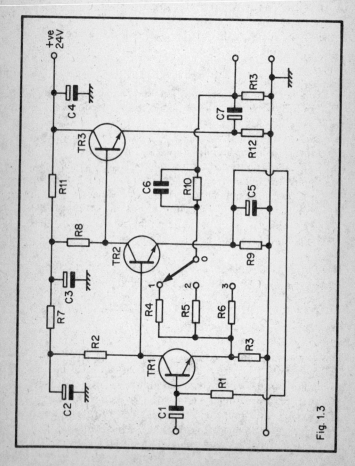

Fig. 1.3

and 4.75 cm/sec. The frequency curves are shown in Fig. 1.4. R7, C2, R11, C3 and C4 are decoupling networks for each stage. C7 is the output capacitor. The circuit has input impedance (150 kΩ) and a low output imedpance (< 10 Ω) which can be fed to most control units. S1 is shown in the 19 cm/sec position. Positions 2 and 3 are for 9.5 cm/sec and 4.75 cm/sec respectively.

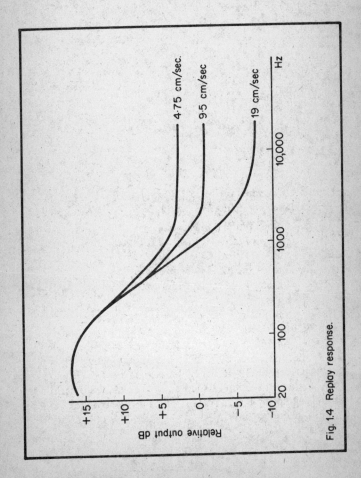

Fig. 1.4 Replay response.

Parts List

Printed circuit board, 14 cm x 9 cm

Transistors:

| TR1, TR3 | BC109 |
| TR2 | BC108 |

Resistors (all resistors ¼ Watt, 5% except those marked * which sould be 2% if possible):

R1	330 kΩ
R2	100 kΩ
R3*	220 Ω
R4*	22 kΩ
R5*	47 kΩ
R6*	82 kΩ
R7	18 kΩ
R8	15 kΩ
R9	820 Ω
R10	2.0 MΩ
R11	3.3 kΩ
R12	3.3 kΩ
R13	220 kΩ

Capacitors:

C1	5 μF/25V Electrolytic
C2	6.4 μF/25V Electrolytic
C3	250 μF/25V Electrolytic
C4	320 μF/25V Electrolytic
C5	160 μF/6V Electrolytic
C6	3.3nF/63V Polystyrene
C7	5 μF/25V Electrolytic

Figs 1.5 and 1.6 show the component and printed circuit sides of the P.C.B. respectively. The shaded section of Fig. 1.6 should be etched out leaving the clear area, which is the final copper print. The P.C.B. is actual size and the layout has been made larger than normal to help beginners. Consult the last section of the book for a detailed description of making up the P.C.B. and the precautions to be taken in mounting components.

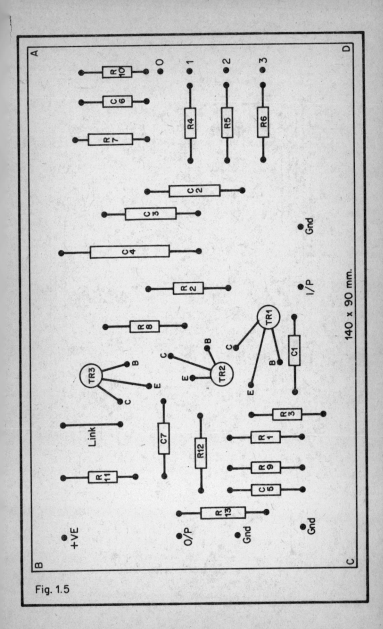

Fig. 1.5

13

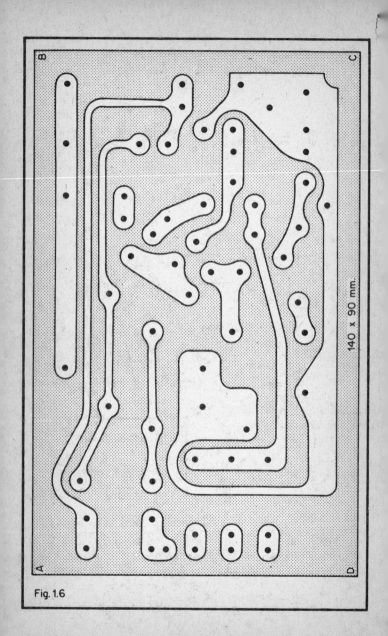

Fig. 1.6

140 x 90 mm.

14

Specifications

Sensitivity . . . . 1 mV at 1 kHz

Gain . . . . 48 dB

Nominal output . . . . 250 mV

Distortion at nominal output 0.1%

Overload capability . . . . 20 dB

Signal/Noise ratio . . . . 54 dB

(B) Three Transistor Circuit

This is a three transistor amplifier with better performance
than (A) (Fig. 1.7). The power supply ripple rejection is
better because the 20 V supply line for TR1 and TR2 is
highly decoupled.

TR1 and TR2 form a high gain amplifier with the closed loop
gain being determined by R5 and the frequency selective
feedback network formed by C21 and R11–R13 connected
between the emitters of TR1 and TR3 via the speed selection
switch S1. R5 also causes the levelling off of gain at 50 Hz,
thus ensuring that the gain does not rise again at very low
frequency.

The collector currents of TR1 and TR2 have been chosen to
be deliberately low, of the order of 100 μA, in order to
achieve a low noise figure. Again there is no high frequency
boost to offset replay head losses. This is due to the fact
that different replay heads require a different amount of
high frequency lift. If you really need it, a starting point
for such a correction would be a simple CR network across
R2. This could be achieved by shunting R2 with a series CR,
with C = 0.05 μF and R = 100 Ω. Further high frequency lift
could be obtained by a slight treble lift in the tone control
unit which would normally follow the pre-amplifier.

TR3 is a conventional emitter follower, providing a high
input impedance to TR2 so that TR2 can have a relatively
high collector load. It has a low output impedance ($<$ 10 Ω).
It is driven from the 30 V decoupled line. This combination

greatly improves the output voltage swing.

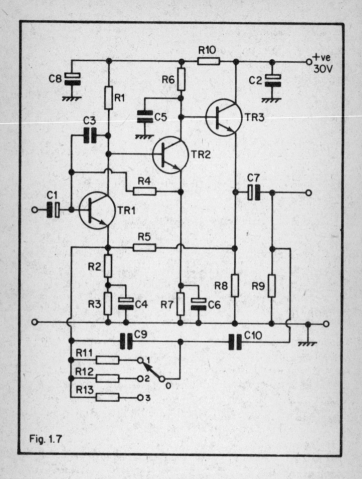

Fig. 1.7

The frequency response curve is shown in Fig. 1.8. This has a roll-off at the upper end of the spectrum and acts as a partial "bias" trap for oscillator frequencies above 50 kHz.

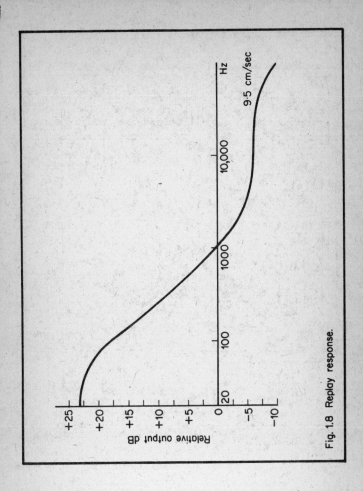

Fig. 1.8 Replay response.

Fig. 1.9 shows the printed circuit pattern and Fig. 1.10 shows the component layout. Etch out the shaded area, leaving the clear area which is the final copper track. The P.C.B. is actual size. Consult the section on P.C.B. at the end of the book for the details about assembly.

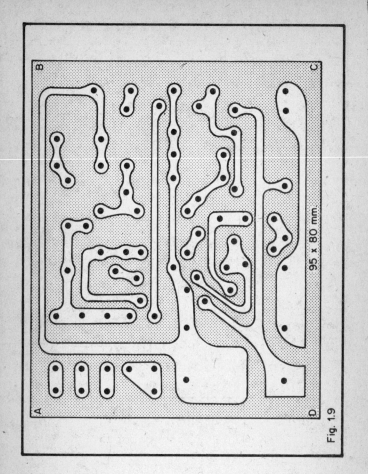

Fig. 1.9

95 x 80 mm

Parts List

Printed circuit board, 9.5 cm x 8.0 cm

Transistors:

TR1, TR2
& TR3 BC109, BC184L, BC184K, 2N3707 (U.S.
JEDEC 2N930, 2N5210, 2N5827, 2N5210)

Resistors (all resistors are ¼ Watt, 5% except those marked *
which should be 2% if possible):

R1 150 kΩ

18

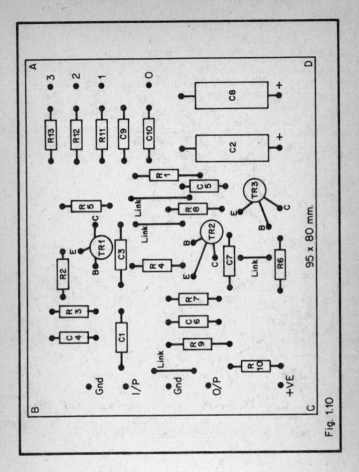

Fig. 1.10

R2*	820 Ω
R3	15 kΩ
R4	56 kΩ
R5*	680 kΩ
R6	100 kΩ
R7	27 kΩ
R8	3.9 kΩ
R9	100 kΩ
R10	47 kΩ

R11*	15 kΩ
R12*	18 kΩ
R13*	27 kΩ

Capacitors:

C1	4 μF/40 V Electrolytic
C2	100 μF/40 V Electrolytic
C3	470 pF/125 V Polystyrene
C4	50 μF/6 V Electrolytic
C5	100 pF/125 V Polystyrene
C6	50 μF/6 V Electrolytic
C7	4 μF/40 V Electrolytic
C8	640 μF/25 V Electrolytic
C9	100 pF/125 V Polystyrene
C10	4.7 nF/63 V Polystyrene

Specifications

Sensitivity . . . . 2 mV
Gain . . . . 42 dB
Nominal output . . . . 250 mV
Distortion at nominal output 0.03%
Overload capability . . . . 34 dB
Signal/Noise ratio . . . . 58 dB

(C) Integrated Circuit Configuration

This circuit uses I.C.s in the form of operational amplifiers (Fig. 1.11). Operational amplifiers possess certain features which make them ideal for pre-amplifiers:—

(a) A very high mid-band gain which permits equalisation and yet retains enough gain to reduce distortion at low levels.

(b) High input impedance and low output impedance which is ideal for the application of feedback as loading effects are minimised.

(c) High supply ripple voltage rejection, i.e. the amplifier will work satisfactorily on unregulated power supply without the possibility of low frequency instability.

(d) Large output voltage swing resulting in good overload properties.

(e) The amplifier will reject any spurious signals that are common to both inputs.

The amplifier uses two 748P I.C.s. Although they are slightly more expensive than the popular 741P, they have a higher gain-bandwidth figure. The input signal is connected to the non-inverting input via a 1 μF capacitor. Frequency compen-

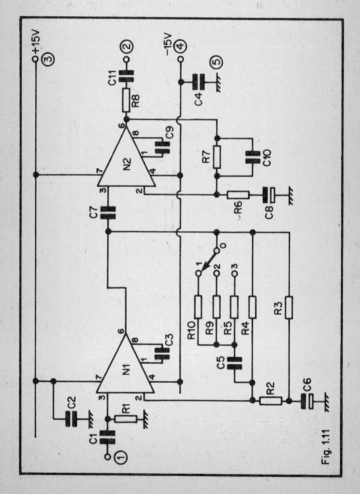

Fig. 1.11

R8 and C11. N1, N2 require 15 V, decoupled by C2 and C4.

Fig. 1.12 shows the frequency response of the amplifier at 9.5 cm/sec. Fig. 1.13 shows the printed circuit and Fig. 1.14 shows the component layout. The clear areas of the printed board should be etched out leaving the finished track. See section on P.C.B. for details on assembly.

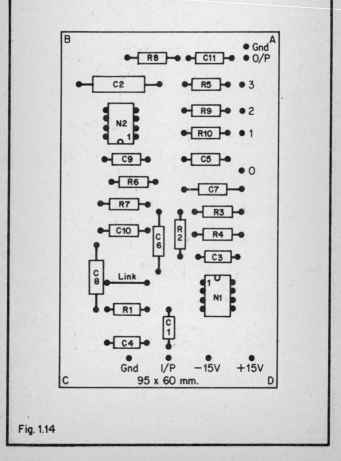

Fig. 1.14

Parts List

Printed circuited board, 9.5 cm x 6 cm

Integrated circuits:

N1, N2	748P

Resistors (all resistors ¼ Watt, 5% except those marked *
which should be 2% if possible):

R1	47 kΩ
R2*	1 kΩ
R3*	100 kΩ
R4*	820 kΩ
R5*	33 kΩ
R6	15 kΩ
R7	82 kΩ
R8	560 Ω
R9*	22 kΩ
R10*	18 kΩ

Capacitors:

C1	1 μF/6 V Electrolytic
C2	0.1 μF Electrolytic
C3	10 pF/30 V Polystyrene
C4	0.1 μF Polystyrene
C5	3.9 nF Polystyrene
C6	100 μF/3 V Tantalum
C7	1 μF/6 V Tantalum
C8	100 μF/3 V Tantalum
C9	10 pF/30 V Polystyrene
C10	47 pF/30 V Polystyrene
C11	10 μF/16 V Tantalum

Specifications

Sensitivity	2 mV
Gain	48 dB
Nominal output	500 mV
Distortion at nominal output	0.05%
Overload capability	38 dB
Signal/Noise ratio	60 dB

impedance and a matching transformer raises the impedance to about 200 Ω. This also increases the output. A disadvantage is that it is prone to bass distortion under close microphone working conditions.

Other types of microphones that are available, but could be expensive for the enthusiast are Condenser Microphones, Advanced Ribbon Microphones, Electret Microphones.

Microphone sensitivity is usually specified in decibels relative to $1V/\mu B$ across a given load. For example, a microphone with a sensitivity of -70 dB/μB across 200 Ω would give an output of 0.3 mV across 200 Ω when subject to a pressure of 1 μB.

The sound pressure at a distance of 1 foot from the microphone in a normal tone of voice (friendly conversation) would be around 10 μB and using the above microphone would give an output of 10 x 0.3 mV = 3 mV.

Typical sound pressures are as follows:

Jet aircraft (not Concorde) at 180 m .... 200 μB
Inside tube train .... 18 μB
Busy street .... 12 μB
Noisy office .... 2 μB
Quiet office .... 0.1 μB
Public library .... 0.02 μB
Grave yard? .... 0.001 μB

Suppose we have a microphone with a sensitivity of -70 dB and an output impedance of 60 Ω say, and we wish to put a step up transformer at the output of the microphone at the microphone end; then the sensitivity and the impedance would change. Suppose it is a 2:1 transformer, then the new impedance would be 2^2 x 60 Ω = 240 Ω. The sensitivity of the microphone on the other hand would change by a factor of 2, i.e. 6 dB to $-$ 64 dB across 240 Ω. Care should always be taken when increase in sensitivity is being considered; because for every 6 dB gained, the source impedance is quadrupled and this defeats the object of having an ideal low impedance microphone. The maximum impedance for a low impedance microphone is usually 600 Ω.

High Impedance Pre-Amp

The first thought that comes to mind when faced with a high source impedance is to use a transformer to convert the

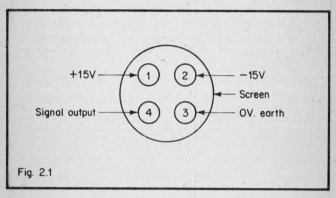

Fig. 2.1

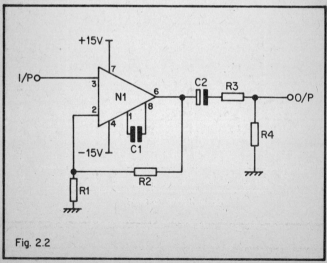

Fig. 2.2

gain of just over unity (1.4). Resistors R1, R2 have been chosen for minimum drift. The noise level is very low. The output impedance is also very low. The frequency response is fairly flat as is shown in Fig. 2.3 and the circuit diagram is shown in Fig. 2.2. The low frequency end of the response can be altered by a suitable choice of C2. Reduction of the value of C2 results in the fall of the low frequency response. Because of the low gain, the distortion is very low and even for a sensitivity of 0 dB (1 V/μB), the distortion is less than 0.1%.

The printed circuit board and component layout are shown in Figs 2.4 and 2.5 respectively.

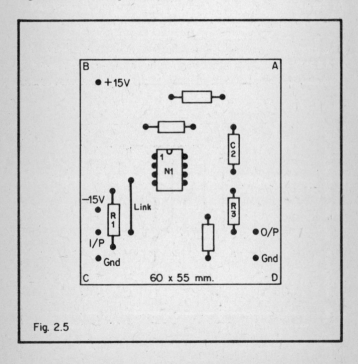

Fig. 2.5

Parts List

Printed circuit board, 6.0 cm x 5.5 cm

Integrated circuit:

N1   SN72748P

Resistors (all resistors ¼ Watt, 10% unless otherwise specified):

R1	4.7 MΩ
R2	2.2 MΩ
R3	510 Ω
R4	10 kΩ

Capacitors:

C1	10 pF/30 V Polystyrene
C2	1 MF/16 V Electrolytic

Specifications

Sensitivity . . . . 180 mV for 250 mV output

Frequency response . . . . 40 Hz – 20 kHz –1dB

Distortion at nominal output . . . . < 0.05%

Overload margin (0.1% distortion) . . . . 23 dB

Noise output . . . . 0.3 mV

Low Impedance Pre-Amp

The pre-amplifier unit consists of an input transformer, a sensitivity switch and the main amplifier (Fig. 2.6). The input transformer has an input impedance of 250 ohms and a turns ratio of 14:1. This results in a secondary impedance of 50 kΩ and a gain of 23 dB. The input transformer accepts signals up to 2.0 mV. The transformer feeds the sensitivity switch. The sensitivity switch is in two sections. One section adjusts the input to the amplifier and the other section is in the feedback loop and hence adjusts the closed loop gain. In effect, we have a two-position sensitivity switch – low sensitivity microphone position giving a high gain and a higher sensitivity position giving a relatively low gain.

The amplifier is a conventional operational amplifier, with the signal being fed to the non-inverting input via capacitor C1. R1, C2 form a simple low pass filter with a turnover frequency of 20 kHz. Feedback is employed from the output to the inverting input via an isolating capacitor C3 and the second section of the sensitivity switch. The inverting input has a low input impedance.

The amplifier is powered by ± 15 V supply and is decoupled by C5 and C6. The amplifier has a low output impedance and R4 is a built-up impedance. It has adequate overload capability. The frequency response is shown in Fig. 2.7.

As stated earlier, the gain of the amplifier is controlled by the feedback section of the sensitivity switch. The gain is given by (R7 + R8)/R9. The gain can be made variable by replacing (R7 + R8) by three resistors as shown, this arrangement gives a gain variation range of 38dB (Fig. 2.6a).

The amplifier could be used without a transformer, but this reduces the sensitivity of the amplifier by about 25 dB and the low/high sensitivity facility is then lost. The modified circuit is shown in Fig. 2.8.

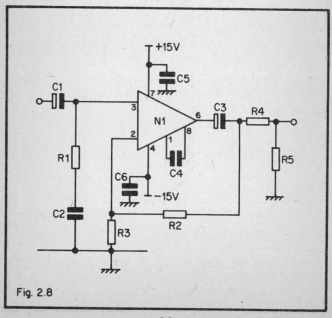

Fig. 2.8

36

The printed circuit and component layout are shown in Figs 2.9 and 2.10 rsepectively. When the circuit of Fig. 2.8 is used, link AB on the P.C. board and R2 = R7 + R8, R3 = R9.

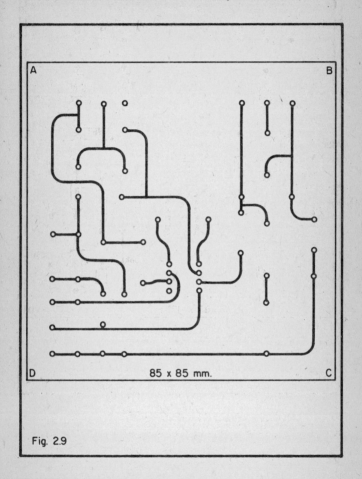

Fig. 2.9

Parts List
Printed circuit board 8.5 cm x 8.5 cm
Integrated circuit:
N1   SN72748P

Section 3

DISC PRE-AMPLIFIERS

A disc (record) is made by a cutting stylus cutting grooves on a blank lacquer. The modulation (music, speech, etc.) being contained in the grooves. The grooves are usually cut at constant amplitude and the information is contained in the variation of the stylus velocity at any point. Hence the instantaneous velocity of the stylus is an indication of the level (loudness) of the signal at that point. At low frequencies, the velocity is low and at high frequencies the velocity is high. The result of this is that the level on the disc is higher at high frequencies than at lower frequencies, thus improving the signal to noise ratio and preventing distortion at low and medium frequencies, as an examination of the energy spectrum of music shows that there is little energy at high frequencies. This has been adopted as a standard and forms the basis of the Disc Recording Characteristics commonly known as the RIAA (Recording Industry Association of America) curve. Fig. 3.1 shows this curve.

It is the usual practice to measure the sound level on a disc in cm/sec. The standard reference level is 5 cm/sec. Peak velocities as high as 25 cm/sec have been known to have been cut on some "popular" discs in the mid-frequency range and no doubt as the technology of disc cutters improves, this would be a common practice.

The complementary process of reproducing the disc is carried out by the pick-up. The most popular methods of signal generation are the piezo electric and the electromagnetic. .

Piezo Electric Cartridges

Two types of piezo electric cartridges come under this heading: the "crystal" pick-up which is used in the cheaper type of disc players has a limited performance and is not very kind

41

The response of this circuit approximates the recording curve and hence the output could be connected to a magnetic pick-up input socket. As only three components are required, they could be mounted across the pre-amplifier input socket.

High Output Pick-Up:

Parts List
Printed circuit board, 7 cm x 7 cm
Integrated circuit:

N1	S72748P

Resistors (all resistors ¼ Watt, unless otherwise specified):

R1	3.3 MΩ
R2	2.2 MΩ
R3	510 Ω
R4	10 kΩ

Capacitors:

C1	20 pF
C2	10 μF/16 V Tantalum
C3	100 μF/16 V Tantalum

Specification
Sensitivity . . . . 100 mV for 250 mV output
Distortion . . . . < 0.1%
Signal to noise ratio . . . . −70 dB rel 2 V
Overload capability . . . . 25 dB

Low Output Pick-up:

Parts List
Printed circuit board, 7 cm x 7 cm
Integrated circuit:

N1	SN72748P

Resistors (all resistors ¼ Watt):

R1	47 kΩ
R2	6.8 kΩ
R3	1.2 kΩ
R4	510 Ω
R5	10 kΩ

Capacitors:

C1	20 pF
C2	5 μF/16 V Tantalum
C3	100 μF/3 V Tantalum
C4	10 μ/16 V

Specification

Sensitivity . . . . 30 mV for 250 mV output
Distortion . . . . < 0.1%
Signal to noise ratio . . . . −70 dB rel 2 V
Overload capability . . . . 25 dB

Magnetic Cartridges

The other type of cartridge is the device which generates its
output purely by electromagnetic principles: hence the
magnetic cartridge. Unlike the ceramic cartridge, the output
from the cartridge increases with the increase in velocity of the
cartridge. The sensitivity of the cartridge averages 2 mV/cm/sec
and as stated earlier with modulation of 25 cm/sec, we can
expect signal level approaching 50 mV. Also to be considered
is adequate signal to noise at nominal signal level of 5 mV
when considering "classical" discs. The third aspect to be
considered is frequency response. As the ideal could not be
achieved, it becomes a compromise between signal to noise
ratio, greater than 60 dB; adequate overload margin, greater
than 35 dB; and the variation of frequency response above
10 kHz due to the capacitance of the connecting input cable
and the reflected reactance of equalisation network.

As a result of the above, the pre-amplifier has been divided
into two sections as shown in Fig. 3.9.

The amplifier N1 has a gain of 25 with RIAA equalisation in
the feedback loop. This amplifier raises the signal from a
nominal 2 mV to 50 mV. This stage has a good signal to noise
ratio (60 dB) and a distortion of 0.05% at an output of 3 V.
As the nominal output is 50 mV, we have an overload margin
38 dB. N2 has a gain of 5 with a simple resistive network in

response of the amplifier is shown in Fig. 3.11.

Figs 3.12 and 3.13 show the printed circuit board and the component layout. It is advisable to use a low loss cable from the pick-up to the pre-amplifier. Use a coaxial cable with a maximum capacitance of 150 pF.

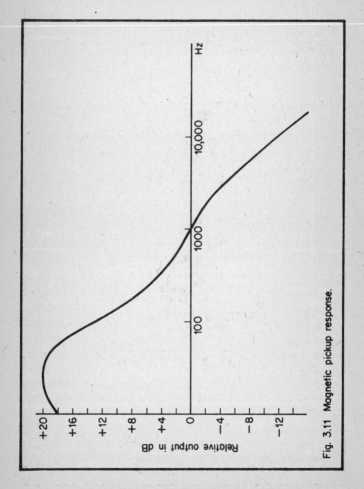

Fig. 3.11 Magnetic pickup response.

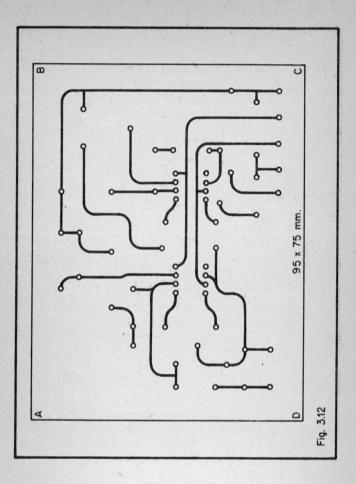

B

C

95 x 75 mm.

A

D

Fig. 3.12

Parts List

Printed circuit board, 9.5 cm x 7.5 cm

Integrated circuit:

N1, N2   SN72748P

Resistors (all resistors ¼ Watt, 10% except those marked *
which are ¼ Watt 5%):

R1   47 kΩ

R2*   1 kΩ

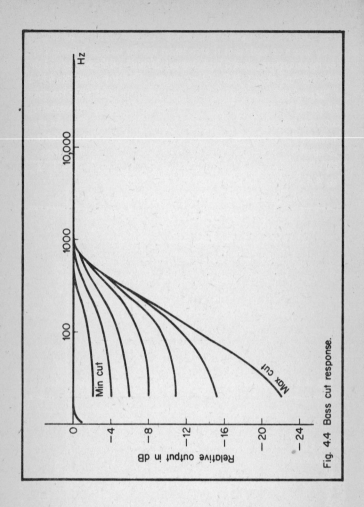

Fig. 4.4 Bass cut response.

Bass Boost

Unlike the two previous circuits there is some attenuation in the passband. In fact, bass boost is achieved by attenuating the mid and high frequencies to a fixed level and then varying the level at the low frequency end using R1.

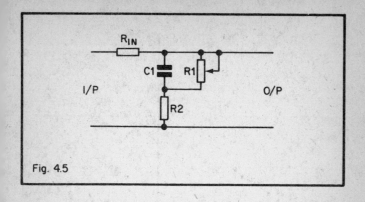

Fig. 4.5

In the circuit (Fig. 4.5) the source impedance is so important, that I have decided to make it part of the circuit. At mid and high frequencies, C1 has a low impedance and the output is given by $R2/(R_{IN}+ R2)$ times the input signal or the fixed attentuation is given by $1+ (R_{IN}/R2)$. In this particular case, the attenuation is 2 or 6 dB. Again we assume that the source has a low impedance and R_{IN} is a built-up resistance. For example, if the source resistance is 600Ω, then $R_{IN} = 5k\Omega - 600 \Omega = 4.4 k\Omega$ (4.3 kΩ). At very low frequency, the impedance of C1 is relatively high and R1 shunts this impedance, thus varying the response at the low frequency end. The response is shown in Fig. 4.6. Maximum boost occurs with R1 fully in circuit. Again the load of the unit should be high, of the order of 50 kΩ.

Parts List
Resistors (all resistors ¼ Watt, 5%):
R1   100 kΩ lin
R2   5.1 kΩ
Capacitors:
C1   0.15 μF

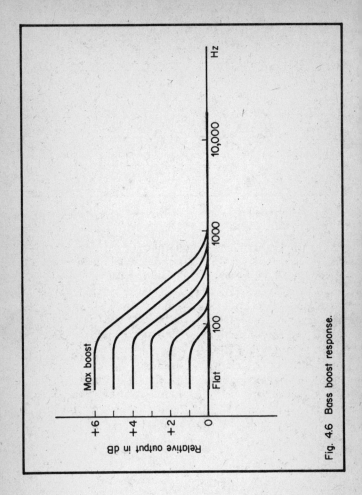

Fig. 4.6 Bass boost response.

Treble Cut (Fig. 4.7)

The frequency dependent components are across the load and the source resistance forms part of the network. As in the previous case, R1 is selected such that together with the assumed low resistance, the total resistance is 5.1 kΩ. Assuming a source resistance of 600 Ω, then R1 is 4.3 kΩ. When R2 is fully out of circuit, maximum treble cut occurs with a turnover frequency of 6 kHz. The response then falls at 6 dB per octave. Minimum cut occurs when R2 is fully in circuit. The circuit should look into a high resistance of the order of 500 kΩ or more. The response is shown in Fig. 4.8.

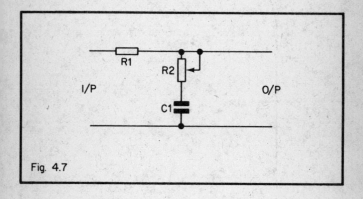

Fig. 4.7

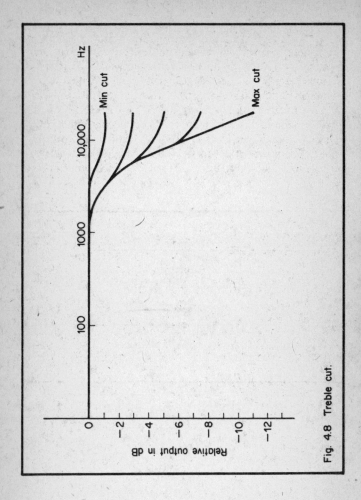

Fig. 4.8 Treble cut.

Treble Boost (Fig. 4.9)

In this circuit, the series arm provides two paths for the signal depending on the frequency. The low and middle frequencies go through R3 and together with R5 forms a simple potential divider and the signal is attenuated to a fixed level. The high frequency signal goes through R4, C2 and across R5. C2 has a relatively low impedance at high frequency and with R4 out of circuit, we have maximum boost. As with the Bass Boost circuit, Treble Boost is achieved at the expense of low and mid frequency attenuation and the maximum boost is 6 dB. The source resistance should be low and the load of the unit should be high. The response is shown in Fig. 4.10.

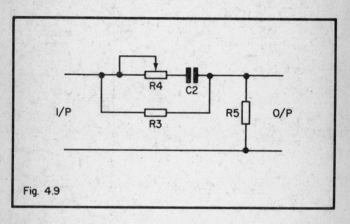

Fig. 4.9

Parts List
Resistors (all resistors ¼ Watt, 5%):

R1	4.3 kΩ
R2	100 kΩ lin
R3	4.7 kΩ
R4	25 kΩ lin
R5	2.2 kΩ

Capacitors:

C1	4.7 nF
C2	4.7 nF

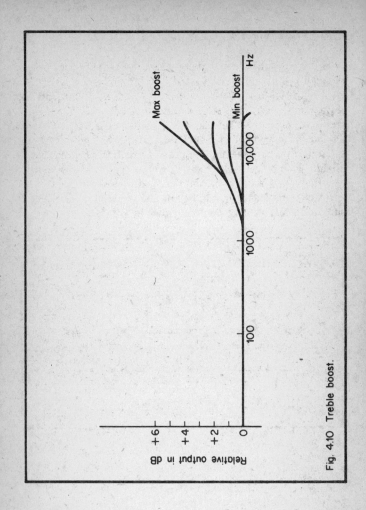

Fig. 4.10 Treble boost.

Comprehensive Tone Control (Fig. 4.11)

This is a very conventional circuit which incorporates Bass Boost and Cut, Treble Boost and Cut. This type of Tone Control is very popular even in very expensive units.

This type of circuit has some limitation. For instance, if a programme material sounds too "brilliant", what might be needed is a reduction of 2 – 3 dB at 3 kHz. But in order to achieve this, we also introduce a cut of about 8 – 10 dB at 10 kHz. Now this totally upsets the balance of the programme and the more we try to correct this, the worse the situation gets. The same reasoning applies to the boost effect. The result could be disastrous as distortion might also be introduced especially if the source is a disc. What is actually needed is a "presence" unit.

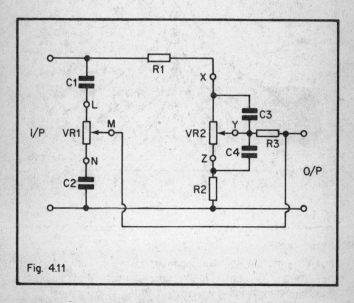

Fig. 4.11

The circuit diagram is shown in Fig. 4.11 – C1, C2 have a high impedance at low frequency and so VR1 is ineffective in controlling the low frequency signal. At high frequency they

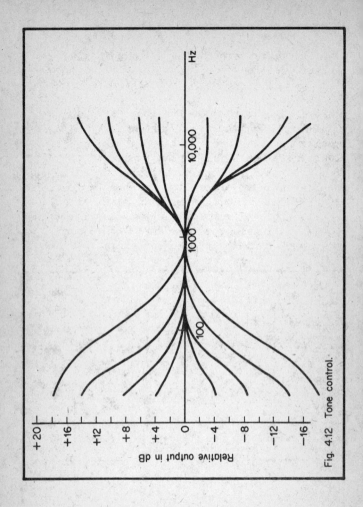

Fig. 4.12 Tone control.

have a comparatively low impedance and VR1 then controls
the output of the unit at high frequency. C3, C4 by-pass the
high frequency signals to earth via R2. R1 is high enough to
ensure that the signal is not shorted to earth. At low frequency, C3, C4 have a high impedance and VR2 shorts this
impedance. Thus VR2 controls the output at low frequency.
R1 also isolates the inputs to both circuits and R3 isolates

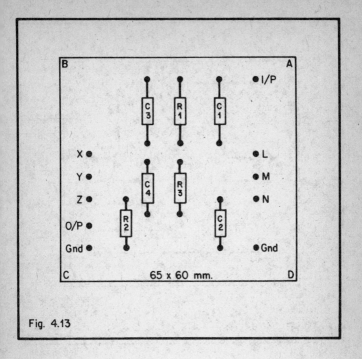

Fig. 4.13

both outputs. In view of this there is an interaction of the controls.

Fig. 4.12 shows the response of the unit, Figs 4.13 and 4.14 show the component layout and printed circuit board respectively.

Parts List
Printed circuit board, 6.5 cm x 6 cm
Resistors (all resistors ¼ Watt, 5%):

R1	10 kΩ
R2	1 kΩ
R3	1.5 kΩ
VR1	100 kΩ lin
VR2	100 kΩ lin

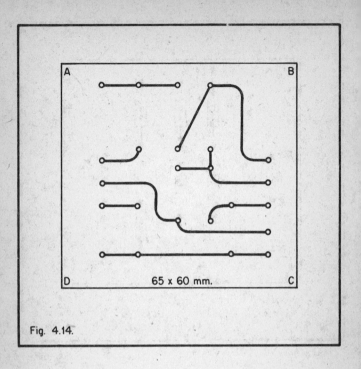

Fig. 4.14.

Capacitors:

C1	4.7 nF
C2	47 nF
C3	47 nF
C4	470 nF

Specification

Passive Tone Control:

Treble . . . . 15 kHz ± 16 dB

Bass . . . . 30 Hz ± 17 dB

So far we have dealt with "passive" tone controls, i.e. no electronic devices such as amplifiers were involved. We will now deal with "active" tone controls. The basic form of an active control is shown in Fig. 4.15.

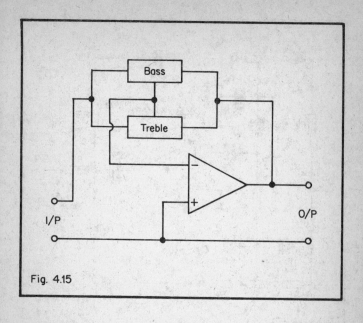

Fig. 4.15

The frequency dependent elements are in the feedback loop.
In the Bass loop, the high and medium frequencies are by-
passed and the Bass control adjusts the gain of the low frequency component of the signal. Similarly, in the Treble loop,
the low frequency signals are by-passed and the gain at high
frequency is controlled by the Treble control. At the extreme
end of these controls, the boost and cut may be excessive and
we can have undesirable effects especially when treble boost is
used. At best, this can be distortion and at worst instability;
though not audible, can adversely affect reproduction. In
order to minimise this effect, resistors are inserted in the series
arms of the respective feedback loops. This limits boost and
cut to about 15 dB which is more practical and very good
engineering practice. Fig. 4.16 shows the circuit diagram.
Because in the "cut" position, 100% of feedback is applied
round the circuit resulting in a unity gain amplifier, I have
used the SN72741 instead of the SN72748. The SN72741
has internal frequency compensation and it belongs to the
group, often referred to as "unconditionally stable" and the

71

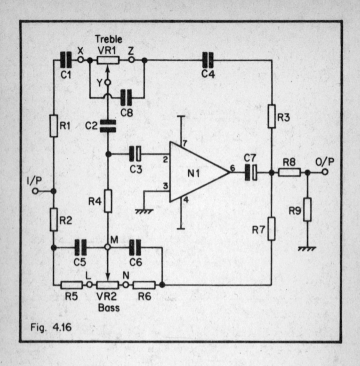

Fig. 4.16

reactive components in the feedback loop have been chosen to maintain this state of affairs.

The input signal is fed to both tone control circuits. At high frequency, C1, C2 and C4 have low impedances and the signal is fed to the inverting input via C1, part of VR1 and C2. Feedback is taken from the output via R3, C4 and part of VR1 and C2 to the inverting input. Hence if VR1 is in the mid position, we have unity gain, as R1, R3 are equal. If the slider of VR1 is moved to the end of VR1 nearer C4, the gain is given by R3/(R1 + VR1) and this gives maximum cut. This is an attenuation of $1 + (VR1/R3)$. This is modified by the impedance of C4 so that the maximum attenuation is 15 dB. When the slider is moved to the other end of VR1, nearer C1, maximum boost is achieved and the gain is given by (R3 + VR1)/R1. Again, this is modified by the impedance of C1 and the maxi-

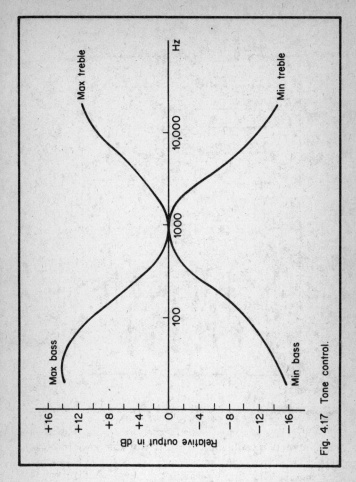

Fig. 4.17 Tone control.

mum boost is limited to 12 dB. At very high frequencies, above 20 kHz, C8 has a shunting effect on VR1 and this effectively limits the maximum boost at very high frequencies. This tends to stabilise the amplifier at high frequency C2 is chosen such that its impedance is low at high frequency and yet at low frequency (100 Hz), its impedance is at least ten times greater than R4. The treble control has negligible effect at low frequency. For the Bass Control, we have maximum

73

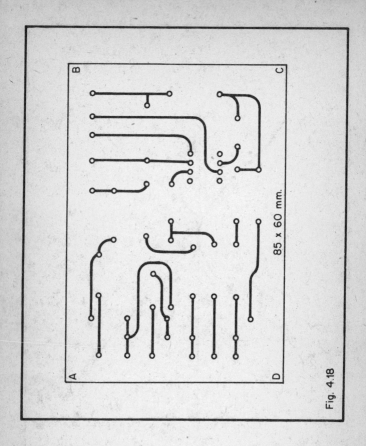

Fig. 4.18

and minimum gain when the Bass Control slider is nearer R2 and R6 respectively. At high frequency C5, C6 have a shunting effect on VR2, thus by-passing the control and the gain is given by R6/R7, i.e. unity. There is however some interaction between VR1 and VR2 at mid frequencies, but this is minimised by the inclusion of R4.

The unit should be fed from a very low impedance source, not greater than 100 Ω, as impedances greater than this might have an effect on Treble cut and boost as R1, R3 are of the order of 1 kΩ. If the source impedance is greater then the

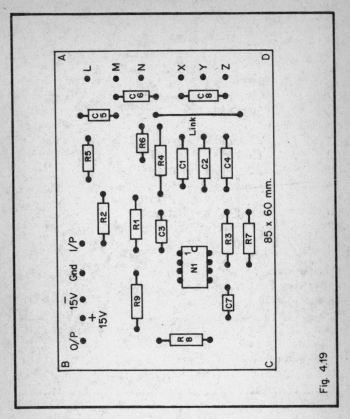

Fig. 4.19

curves will deviate from those shown in Fig. 4.17. Figs 4.18
and 4.19 show the printed circuit board and component
layout respectively.

Parts List
Printed circuit board, 8.5 cm x 6 cm
Integrated circuit:
N1   SN72741P
Resistors (all resistors ¼ Watt, 5%):
R1   1.2 kΩ
R2   6.8 kΩ
R3   1.2 kΩ

R4	12 kΩ
R5	8.2 kΩ
R6	8.2 kΩ
R7	6.8 kΩ
R8	510 Ω
R9	10 kΩ
VR1	10 kΩ lin
VR2	50 kΩ lin

Capacitors:

C1	22 nF/30 V Polystyrene
C2	15 nF/30 V Polystyrene
C3	22 µF/ 16V Electrolytic
C4	22 nF/30 V Polystyrene
C5	22 nF/30 V Polystyrene
C6	22 nF/30 V Polystyrene
C7	10 µF/16 V Electrolytic
C8	150 pF

Specification

Active Tone Control:

Treble	± 12 – 15 dB at 20 kHz
Bass	± 15 dB at 30 Hz
Gain	unity at 1 kHz
Distortion	0.25%
Overload capability	26 dB
Signal to noise ratio	65 dB

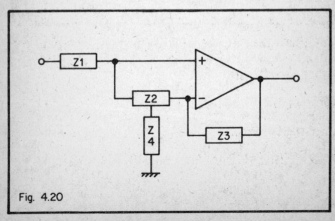

Fig. 4.20

Presence Unit

As stated earlier, the presence unit is a more desirable unit
than the treble tone control. When we have a programme
material that is dull, all that is needed is a slight boost in the
upper middle frequency range. If a tone control is used to
correct this, we will have excessive boost of the order of
12 dB at 10 kHz in order to achieve 2 to 3 dB at 3 kHz say.
This is very objectionable as the musical balance is upset,
apart from distortion consideration. Conversely, if the
programme sounds too "brilliant", we have to introduce
3 dB cut at 3 kHz, say; again this introduces excessive cut
at 10 kHz and a lack of "bite" in the sound. With a
presence unit, boost or cut is applied over a limited band of
frequencies as is shown below. The form of the presence unit
is shown in Fig. 4.20.

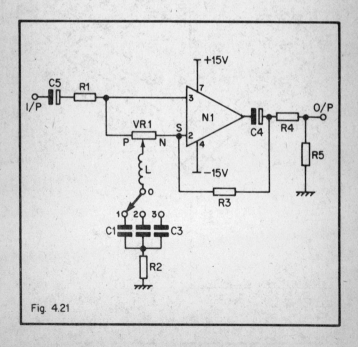

Fig. 4.21

The input to the amplifier is made up of two signals. Input A is fed to the inverting input of the amplifier via Z1, Z2 and feedback from the output is via Z3. The gain of this route is Z3/(Z1 + Z2). Z1, Z2, Z3 being purely resistive, the output from this input is independent of frequency. Input B is via Z1 to the non-inverting input of the amplifier. Feedback to the inverting input is via Z3 and Z4. Because Z4 is made up L, C, R the output contribution from this input is fre-

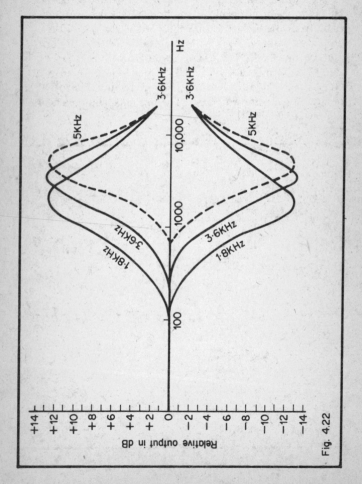

Fig. 4.22

quency dependent and we achieve selective frequency amplification. The circuit is shown in Fig. 4.21.

The integrated circuit used is the SN72741P, Z4 is made up of a coil, switchable capacitance and R2. R2 has been included to damp the tuned circuit so that the response is not too sharp. The gain of the frequency dependent section is given by (R3 + part of VR1 + Z4)/(part of VR1 + Z4). As we move away from the resonant frequency, due to L, C1 say, the impedance of Z4 increases rapidly to give the familiar "bell shaped" response. The unit has a three position switch for the centre frequencies 1.8 kHz, 3.6 kHz and 5 kHz. The unit should be fed from a low impedance source. The output

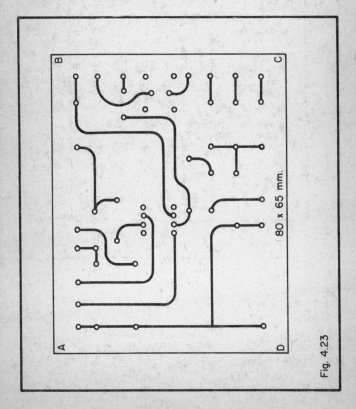

Fig. 4.23

79

impedance of the unit is low and it has adequate overload capability. The response is shown in Fig. 4.22. Figs 4.23 and 4.24 show the printed circuit board and component layout respectively.

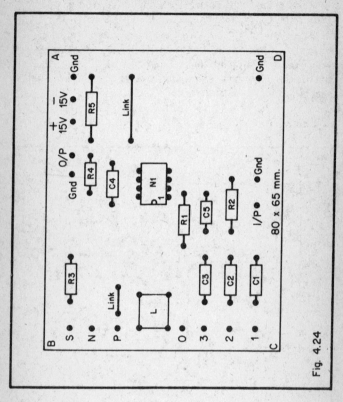

Fig. 4.24

Parts List
Printed circuit board, 8 cm x 6.5 cm
Integrated circuit:
N1   SN72741P
Resistors (all resistors ¼ Watt, 10% unless marked * when they should be ¼ Watt, 5%):
R1   3.3 kΩ
R2   910 Ω

R3	3.3 kΩ
R4	510 Ω
R5	10 kΩ
VR1	5 kΩ lin

Capacitors:

C1	800 nF/30 V
C2	220 nF/30 V
C3	82 nF/30 V
C4	10 μF/16 V
C5	10 μF/16 V

Coil:

L1	11.7 mH

Specification

Switchable frequencies . . . . 1.8 kHz, 3.6 kHz, 5 kHz
Response . . . . bell shaped ± 13 dB
Distortion 0.08%
Overload capability . . . . 20 dB
Signal to noise ratio . . . 60 dB rel 250 mV (nominal output)

Section 5

FILTERS

Filters are classified into three main categories:

(i)   Low Pass – they pass all frequencies below a critical frequency fc.
(ii) High Pass – they pass all frequencies above a critical frequency fc.
(iii) Band Pass – they pass frequencies between two frequencies, f_1 and f_2

High Pass Filter

This is a simple second order filter with a cut-off frequency at 35 Hz (Fig. 5.1).

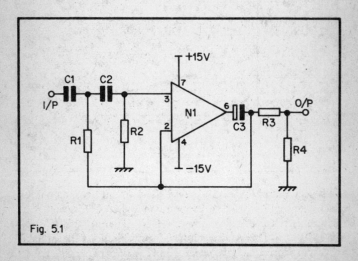

Fig. 5.1

N1 is a buffer amplifier with a gain of unity in the passband. At frequencies lower than the cut-off frequency, fc, the gain

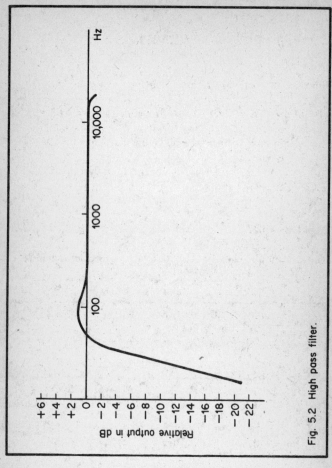

Fig. 5.2 High pass filter.

falls very sharply at 12 dB/octave. The circuit has a damping factor of 0.5 to obtain the response indicated in Fig. 5.2. The damping factor is given by $\sqrt{(R1/R2)}$. There is slight peak of 1 dB at 70 Hz. A disadvantage of this circuit is that it has a varying input impedance of 40 kΩ − 200 kΩ. This is adequate for most purposes except where the preceeding source is capacitive such as a ceramic pick-up. The output impedance of the unit is low. The printed circuit board

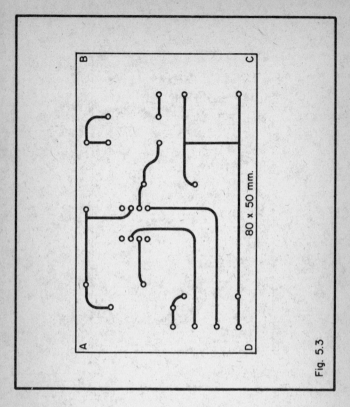

Fig. 5.3

and component layout are shown in Figs 5.3 and 5.4
respectively.

Parts List

Printed circuit board, 8 cm x 5 cm

Integrated circuit:

N1   SN72741P

Resistors (all resistors ¼ Watt, 5%):

R1   12 kΩ
R2   47 kΩ
R3   510 Ω
R4   10 kΩ

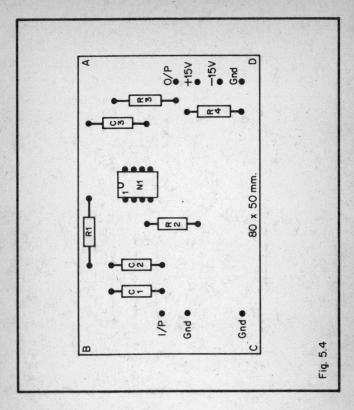

Fig. 5.4

Capacitors:
C1   0.2 μF
C2   0.2 μF
C3   10 μF/16 V

Specification
Second order High Pass Filter:
Cut-off frequency . . . . 35 Hz
Roll-off . . . . 12 dB/octave
Peaking . . . . 70 Hz 1 dB

Low Pass Filter

This is similar in form to the High Pass Filter with the resistor and capacitor positions interchanged at the input (Fig. 5.5).

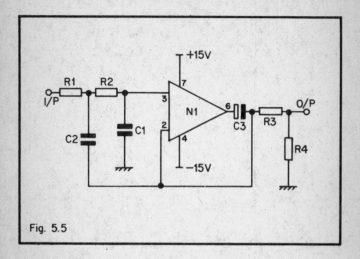

Fig. 5.5

The same principle applies here. The unit has a 12 dB/octave fall above the cut-off frequency, fc. The damping factor is given by $\sqrt{(C1/C2)}$. There is a peak of 1 dB at 20 kHz as is shown in the response curve in Fig. 5.6. The unit has a low output impedance and a varying high input impedance. Figs 5.7 and 5.8 show the printed circuit board and component layout.

Parts List
Printed circuit board, 8 cm x 5 cm
Integrated circuit:
N1   SN72741P
Resistors (all resistors ¼ Watt, 5%):
R1   22 kΩ
R2   22 kΩ
R3   510 Ω
R4   10 kΩ

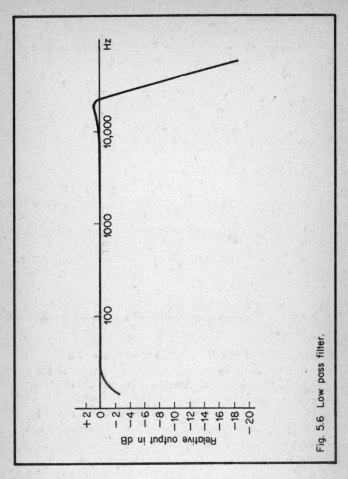

Fig. 5.6 Low pass filter.

Capacitors:
C1   150 pF Polystyrene
C2   500 pF Polystyrene
C3   10 μF/16 V

88

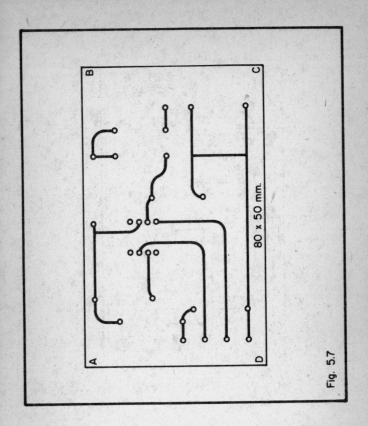

Fig. 5.7

Specification

Second Order Low Pass Filter:

Cut-off frequency .... 25 kHz
Roll-off .... 12 dB/octave
Peaking .... 1 dB at 20 kHz

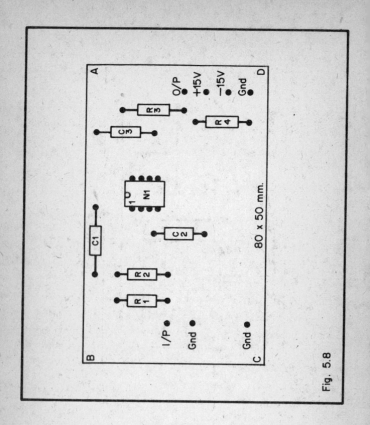

Fig. 5.8

Rumble Filter

Mechanical vibration of the turntable gives rise to unwanted
low frequency noises which become objectionable on low level
passages of music. This situation is made worse by the equalisation process in the pre-amplifier which introduces bass lift.
The rumble signal from a good turntable is around −60 dB
relative to normal operating level.

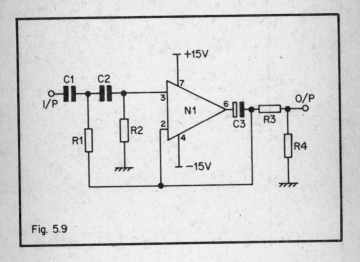

Fig. 5.9

The rumble filter is very similar to the high pass filter des-
cribed earlier, but with a different cut-off frequency. It is
always a compromise between good bass response and mini-
misation of rumble. The input impedance varies in a similar
way to the high pass filter. Although it has no significant
effect when it terminates a magnetic pick-up, the effect is
significant when it terminates a conversion unit of a ceramic
pick-up for use with a magnetic pre-amplifier. The circuit
is shown in Fig. 5.9.

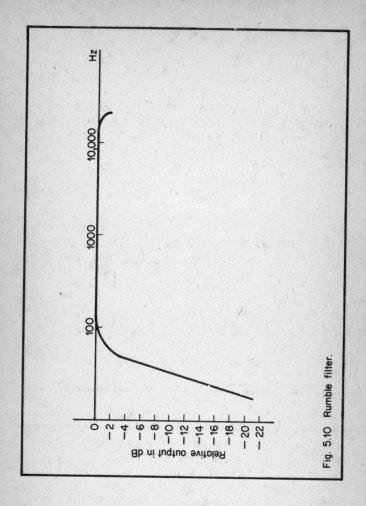

Fig. 5.10 Rumble filter.

The circuit is critically damped. The response is shown in Fig. 5.10. The printed circuit board and component layout are shown in Figs 5.11 and 5.12 respectively.

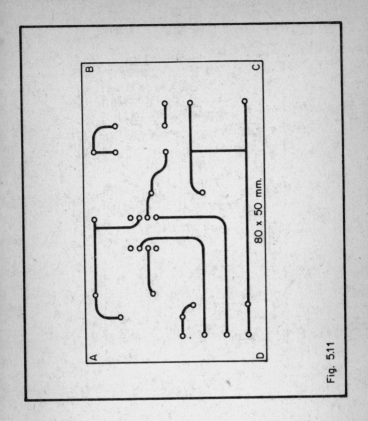

Fig. 5.11

Parts List
Printed circuit board, 8 cm × 5 cm
Integrated circuit:
N1   SN72741P
Resistors (all resistors ¼ Watt, 5%):
R1   22 kΩ
R2   47 kΩ
R3   510 Ω
R4   10 kΩ
Capacitors:
C1   0.1 µF
C2   0.1 µF
C3   10 µF/16 V

93

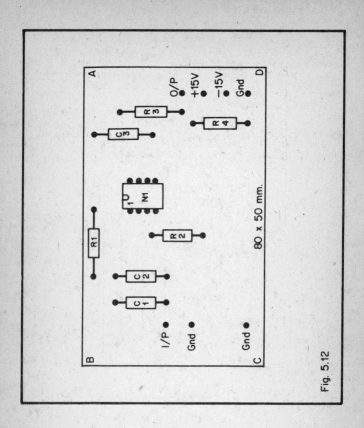

Fig. 5.12

Specification

Second Order Filter, critically damped:

Cut-off frequency . . . . 50 Hz

Roll-off . . . . 12 dB/octave

Scratch Filter

As more people are now playing their old 78 r.p.m. discs on modern equipment, the problem of noise from the shellac disc rears its ugly head and we have to revert to the scratch filter in order to enjoy the music.

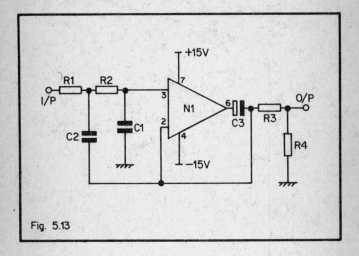

Fig. 5.13

Again this is a second order low pass filter with a cut-off frequency of 6 kHz. A lower cut-off frequency would be unacceptable. The circuit is shown in Fig. 5.13.

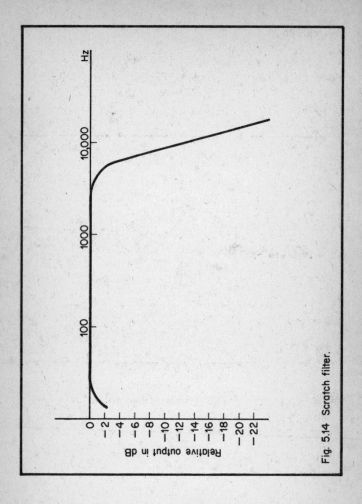

Fig. 5.14 Scratch filter.

The response is shown in Fig. 5.14. Figs 5.15 and 5.16 show the printed circuit board and component layout respectively.

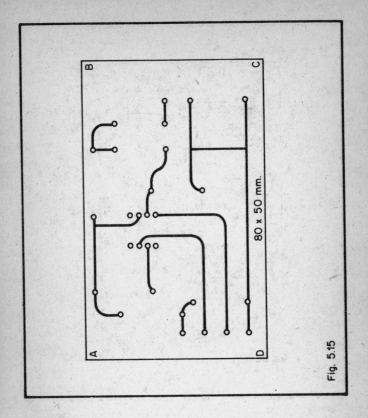

Fig. 5.15

Parts List
Printed circuit board, 8 cm x 5 cm
Integrated circuit:
N1   SN72741P
Resistors (all resistors ¼ Watt, 5%):
R1   22 kΩ
R2   22 kΩ
R3   510 Ω
R4   10 kΩ
Capacitors:
C1   820 pF
C2   1.5 nF
C3   10 μF/16 V

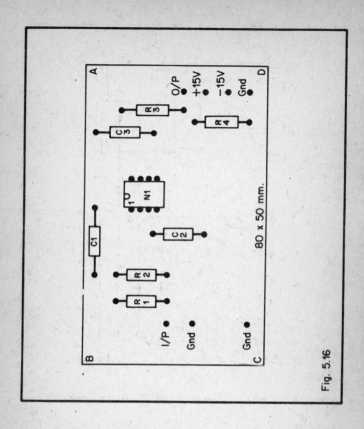

Fig. 5.16

Specification

Second Order Filter, critically damped:

Cut-off frequency .... 6 kHz

Roll-off .... 12 dB/octave

Telephone Simulation

This is a simple bandpass filter with a frequency response that resembles the channel of a telephone. When a full frequency programme is passed through this unit, the output simulates a telephone conversation. The circuit is shown in Fig. 5.17.

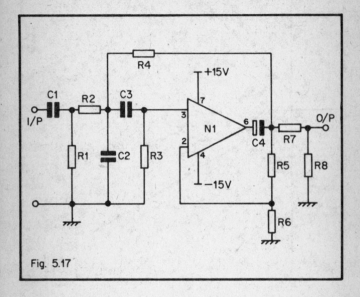

Fig. 5.17

The input signal goes through a simple high pass filter, C1, R1; with a turnover frequency at 700 Hz. The signal then goes through a low pass filter, R2, C2 with a turnover frequency of 2.4 kHz followed by a high pass filter with a turnover frequency of 1 kHz. This results in a bass cut with an initial roll-off of 6 dB/octave and increasing very sharply to 12 dB/octave. The high frequency end falls off at 6 dB/octave.

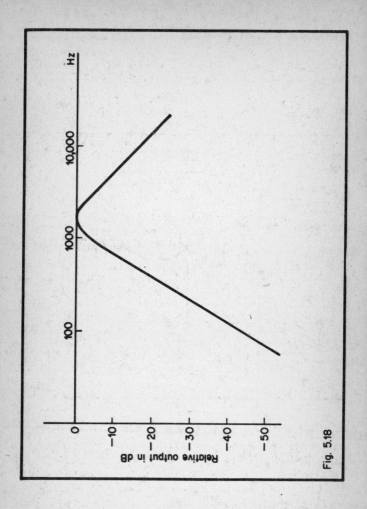

Fig. 5.18

The output of this network is fed to the non-inverting input of
the amplifier. Feedback is taken from the output to the
inverting input via R5, R6. The circuit has a Q of 1.3, the
ratio of the centre frequency to the −3 dB bandwidth. The
response is shown in Fig. 5.18. The printed circuit board and
component layout are shown in Figs 5.19 and 5.20 respectively.

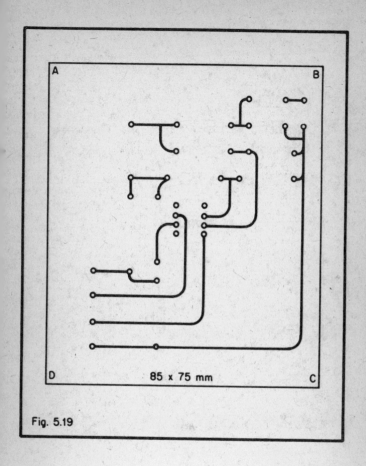

A B

D C

85 x 75 mm

Fig. 5.19

Parts List
Printed circuit board, 8.5 cm x 7.5 cm
Integrated circuit:
N1   SN72741P
Resistors (all resistors ¼ Watt, 5%):
R1   10 kΩ
R2   33 kΩ
R3   62 kΩ
R4   33 kΩ

101

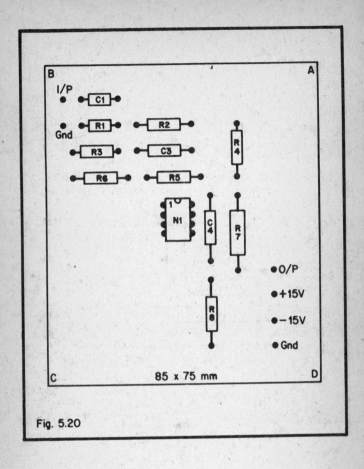

Fig. 5.20

R5	12 kΩ
R6	10 kΩ
R7	510 Ω
R8	10 kΩ

Capacitors:

C1	22 nF
C2	3.3 nF
C3	3.3 nF
C4	10 µF/16 V

102

Section 6

ATTENUATORS AND PADS

When we listen to music from a loudspeaker at a given level, we also set a balance between the high, middle and low frequencies. If this listening level is altered, the whole relationship between the different frequency ranges is altered as well. To minimise this effect, the loudness control was introduced in some hi-fi units. An objective way of looking at the problem is to introduce a step by step volume control preceeding the main power amplifier. Invariably, the power amplifier has an input control. This could then be the "fine" control and the variable attenuator, step by step volume control, is the coarse control. The control has the form shown in Fig. 6.1.

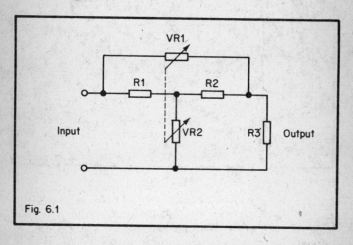

Fig. 6.1

VR1 and VR2 are ganged 11 way switches with resistors across the positions as shown in Figs 6.2 and 6.3. The unit presents a constant resistance to the input and output. For the values stated, the input and output impedances of the unit are 600 Ω. The recommended settings of the attenuator are: +10, +8, +6, +4, +2, Normal, −2, −4, −6, −8, −10 as in

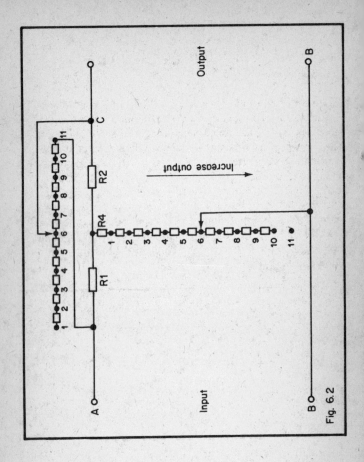

Fig. 6.3. In operation, the coarse control is set to "normal" and the "fine" control is then adjusted to the required listening level. The coarse control could then be adjusted for different listening conditions in fixed steps of 2 dB, when listening to a relatively low modulation disc. The advantage of this system is that it establishes a standard listening level and it makes it easier to assess technical problems such as noise, distortion, etc.

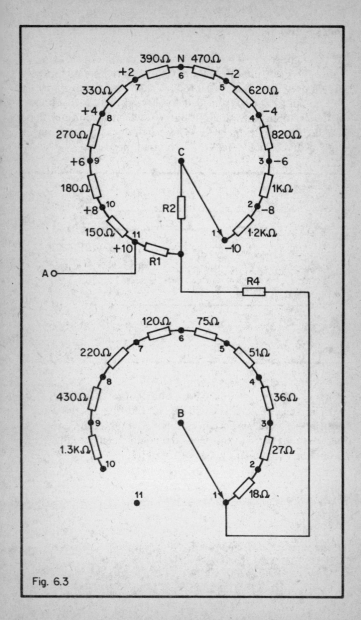

Fig. 6.3

Dim Control

As the name implies, this control attenuates the signal being
fed to the main amplifier, when listening is temporarily inter-
rupted or when it is essential to lower the level by an appreci-
able amount. The advantage of this arrangement is that none
of the continuously variable controls, which might alter the
sound balance, are touched. The arrangement is shown in
Fig. 6.4 and it includes a "CUT" or mute position.

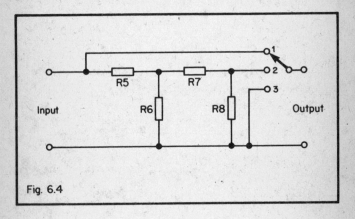

Fig. 6.4

Position 1 is the "normal" position; position 2 is "dim"
with a fixed attenuation of 20 dB and position 3 is the "cut"
position. The values have been calculated for a source resistance of 600 Ω. The unit feeds the volume control. Fig. 6.5
shows the component layout of the unit.

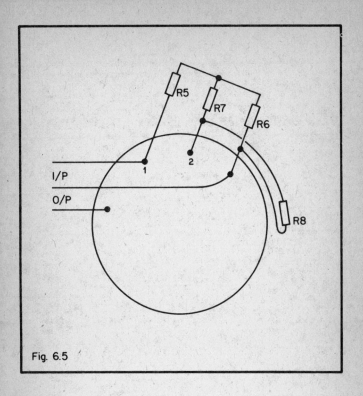

Fig. 6.5

Parts List
Resistors (all resistors ¼ Watt, 5%):

R1	600 Ω
R2	600 Ω
R3	600 Ω
R4	68 Ω
R5	470 Ω
R6	120 Ω
R7	470 Ω
R8	600 Ω

107

Section 7

PRINTED CIRCUIT BOARDS AND ASSEMBLY

A printed circuit board is made up of an insulating base material with a thin layer of copper foil. The base material is either treated paper, fabric or glass fibre. Although fibre glass boards are more expensive, they are better. They are stronger, tolerant to mishandling, easy to work with. There is less risk of chipping when being drilled, less risk of cracking when solder pins or tags are used. Also it is semitranslucent, so that it is quite easy to follow the circuit, if a lamp is put behind the copper side, when viewed from the component side. The finished product looks more professional.

The boards are clad with copper of varying thickness from 25 micron to 75, the current capacity being determined by the width of the copper track. For example, 4 width of track of 25 micron copper can carry 5 A, but the same width of 75 micron copper can carry 15 A.

To process the board, cut the board to size with it still in its plastic package. Remove it from its package, holding it by the edges thus avoiding touching the copper as perspiration moisture that comes into contact with the copper will affect processing. Scrub the board thoroughly using domestic scouring powder. Rinse the powder off under running water, holding it by the edges. Leave to dry in a dirt-free area with copper side facing sideways.

To transfer the pattern from the book to the board, use tracing paper and carbon paper. Put the tracing paper over the book and with a pen or pencil trace the pattern, making sure there is no movement of the paper or the book. Next, put the carbon paper between the tracing paper and the board and slowly trace the pattern onto the board. Using a resist filled pen, which can be bought very cheaply, redraw the pattern on the board. If a resist filled pen is not available, use nail varnish, but ensure that suitable solvent is available. Allow the resist to dry. When dry, fill in any pinholes and smooth out any ragged lines and sharp edges. Check the pattern and the circuit to ensure that no mistakes have been made. Clean off any finger marks or any unwanted resist very thoroughly.

Prepare the etching solution — using a glass or enamel dish as a bath, dissolve the crystals of ferric chloride in water, according to the instructions in the kit. The usual proportion is 1 pint of water to 5 ozs of crystals. A weak solution results in uneven etching and a very strong solution results in over-etching. Alternatively use a prepared solution of ferric chloride.

Put the board in the solution and watch the process very carefully so that over-etching does not occur. Ensure that the solution flows over the board evenly. This could be achieved by rocking the dish. When the etching process is completed, remove from the solution using glass tongs and rinse the board thoroughly under running water. This stops the etching process.

Holes could now be drilled in the board. It is a lot easier if these are marked on the pattern. Clamp the board while drilling to prevent damage to the board and yourself. Using a small scriber, mark the drilling points. Do not make a groove on the pattern with a centre punch. Do not use a portable electric drill, unless mounted on a stand. Use a 1 size drill or a drill No. 66 for all the holes. Larger holes could then be drilled with the appropriate size drills for components like transistors, etc.

Use a resist remover or solvent to remove the marks of the resist pen. Because of the work already done on the board, it might have a lot of foreign matter on the print; hence clean the board with scouring powder. Wash the board and dry with a clean cloth in a warm area. Examine the board for hair-line cracks using a torch and shinning the light from the component side. If there are any cracks, repair with a link of wire. Do not use a blob of solder. Alternatively, if a crack is suspected, flex the board lightly while carrying out a continuity check between the two suspect points or areas. The board is now ready for assembly.

To ensure that the board is neat and looks professional, use the correct size of components. These components are readily available from well known shops in London and big towns. It is also possible to obtain pre-formed components specially formed for p.c.b. assembly. These are recognised by the "kink" in the connecting wires of these components. First, mount any links on the component side of the board with the link as short as possible and very close to the board. Use tinned copper wire for links and where these links are more than 2 inches long, use p.v.c. covered wire. Next mount solder pins and tags. Then resistors and small capacitors and so on until the large components have been mounted. Use transistor pads and integrated circuit holders where possible. To secure the components, bend the ends of the connecting wires over. Always mount the components so that there is no strain on the connecting wires as this often results in bad joints. When you are satisfied that the layout is correct, you can proceed to solder the components.

To avoid dry joints, always tin the connecting wires. Use a 12-watt or 15-watt soldering iron. It helps when soldering to leave the wires as long as possible after they have been bent. Solder the wire, then cut the wire. This helps heat dissipation away from the component itself. As transistors and I.C.s are very sensitive to heat, transistor pads and I.C. holders are very helpful.

Parts List
Printed circuit board
Resist filled pen
Resist solvent
Scouring powder and brush
Ferric chloride crystals or solution
Glass or enamel bath
15-watt soldering iron and solder
Tracing paper and carbon paper.